Advance Praise for

The Rosacea - Acne Natural Remedy

A Recent Discovery On How I Healed

"As a society we have not been taught natural remedies - the kind of self-healing that our ancestors relied on, and we witness the results. Georgie has re-captured this inherent truth." Linda Reilly, Dean of Nursing

"Most of us have trouble trusting those who say they can help us. Georgie is authentic. Her gentle spirit comes from her own healing and that of helping numerous others." TJ Ryan, Radio Talk Show Host

"We hear about healing ourselves and get confused about where to start. Rarely do we find a book by someone who has healed herself, taught thousands of others by her example and writes with unflinching detail. Georgie has paved a path that lets us eliminate the mistakes she made and gives us personal self-help steps to faster recovery." – Robert Lopez, Naturopathic Doctor

Also by Georgie Holbrook:

Joy-Full Holistic Remedies
How to experience your natural ability to heal

A self-help book on holistic healing which looks at the emotional, physical and spiritual well being of a person to find answers to health challenges.

Reprinted since 1999 helping people around the world.

Visit her web site for additional products and services: Joy-Full.com and RosaceaHealedEmotionally.com

The Rosacea – Acne Natural Remedy

A Recent Discovery On How I Healed

Georgie Holbrook

Joy-Full Publishing Co.

The Rosacea - Acne Natural Remedy
A Recent Discovery On How I Healed

Joy-Full Publishing Company
E-mail: Georgie@Joy-Full.com
Web page: Joy-Full.com
Web page: RosaceaHealedEmotionally.com

Harlan Kidwell Jr., long term contributor
Editing by Linda Cashdan, The Word Process
Cover Design and Photograph of author in healthy state
by Don Hernandez, H & H Photography

Library of Congress Cataloging-in-Publication Data
Holbrook, Georgie
The Rosacea - Acne Natural Remedy
ISBN: 978-1-60910-774-1
Library of Congress Catalog Card Number: 2011903813

DISCLAIMER

This book details the author's personal experiences with and opinions about finding Rosacea – Acne solutions. The author is not a healthcare provider.

The author and publisher are providing this book and its contents on an "as is" basis and make no representations or warranties of any kind with respect to this book or its contents. The author and publisher disclaim all such representations and warranties, including for example warranties of merchantability and healthcare for a particular purpose. In addition, the author and publisher do not represent or warrant that the information accessible via this book is complete or current.

The statements made about products and services have not been evaluated by the U.S. Food and Drug Administration. They are not intended to diagnose, treat, cure, or prevent any condition or disease. Please consult with your own physician or healthcare specialist regarding the suggestions and recommendations made in this book.

Except as specifically stated in this book, neither the author or publisher, nor any authors, contributors, or other representatives will be liable for damages arising out of or in connection with the use of this book. This is a comprehensive limitation of liability that applies to all damages of any kind, including (without limitation) compensatory; direct, indirect or consequential damages; loss of data, income or profit; loss of or damage to property and claims of third parties.

You understand that this book is not intended as a substitute for consultation with a licensed healthcare practitioner, such as your physician. Before you begin any healthcare program, or change your lifestyle in any way, you should consult your physician or other licensed healthcare practitioner to ensure that you are in good health and that the examples contained in this book will not harm you.

This book provides content related to topics physical and/or mental health issues. As such, use of this book implies your acceptance of this disclaimer.

Dedicated to the ONE I've Grown to Trust

I dedicate this book to God or the higher Power I've grown to trust, admire and love, who speaks to me in ways I respect and follow and who has taught me I cannot compromise my path to truth, happiness or health.

My body has been my best friend and educator, always calling me to learn more…. to share the discoveries learned from God's University, where I never get to graduate as the next opportunity to prove natural healing happens. I've gotten the inner confidence and knowledge that come from years of my own self-healing and that of working with hundreds of others, only through God's incredible higher plan for my chosen path.

I now can talk at a hospital in front of doctors, staff and interested others and never doubt my truth in self-healing possibilities. Whether I am sharing with people by phone around the world, or standing in person beside a hospital bed, my message is always the same: Walk in faith alongside me until you can learn for yourself through the "experience of self-healing." Many times I've told clients to reach into their hearts and decide to heal to an even greater degree than I did – to prove it for themselves and live by example.

In praise and gratitude God has blessed us with natural remedies. May we walk in faith and not fear our incredible bodies.

Enjoy Georgie

Rosacea - Acne Natural Remedy

A Recent Discovery On How I Healed

Table of Contents

CHAPTER 1

I was Determined to Heal

Currently it is estimated that over 45 million people worldwide suffer from Rosacea and far more from acne. I developed acne that was later diagnosed as an extreme case of Rosacea and near blindness. I holistically healed, I have walked the path before you, so you can eliminate many of the mistakes I made along the way. I believe with understanding anyone can heal even better than I did. I am dedicated to be part of the solution, determined to do my part in helping people reclaim their faces rather than fear them. I want to help avoid future suffering and the low self-esteem along with shame that comes with having Rosacea and acne.

I share from my own experience and my experience working with hundreds of others by phone or in person. I have discovered some obvious emotional and physical indicators of where to find healing answers. I find these indicators are like an obvious flashing red light that has been overlooked by doctors, holistic practitioners and psychotherapists because their search is isolated to the face. Looking for holistic answers means taking the whole person into consideration.

My message is that we are incredibly made, and our minds and bodies are willing and ready to heal; with the proper understanding, we can move from fear to faith.

CHAPTER 2

The Search for Answers

A few years ago, I wrote and self-published a self help book of my healing story which continues to be sold worldwide both in paperback and E-book. *Joy-Full Holistic Remedies, How to experience your natural ability to heal and CDs on additional things I learned about how to heal emotional and physical health challenges.* After writing my book I was left with some questions:

Why had my Rosacea become so extreme? Had I placed so much accumulated stress on my body that my immune system broke down? And if so, how could anyone allow this to happen by being so unaware of herself? What was it I had missed along the way?

I'm going to share with you what I've discovered in hopes of helping you search below the surface of Rosacea and acne for answers.

CHAPTER 3

My Healing Story

If my face could talk – what might it say?
"Stop – you are heading the wrong way
I'll scream louder
and brighter until you are willing to hear – the answer lies
within you -
you have nothing to fear"

Here is my personal healing story and my new discoveries which will lead you into the insights I have gained from working with others, along with self-help tools for your own healing.

I was diagnosed with acne that developed into Rosacea at age 37 at the peak of my corporate career. I first went to my family doctor but he didn't have the answer I was looking for. I ended up going to a skin cancer doctor – not because I thought I had cancer but because I wanted an expert to solve my health challenge and give me a quick fix so I could go back to work. No words could explain the shock and confusion I felt when the doctor said in a matter of fact way that it was "incurable". He had zero doubt! How could he be so convinced? Had he no belief in the human body being capable of healing almost anything? Was he an authority wiser than God?

The word incurable was a foreign concept in my corporate world. I took my diagnosis and decided to do what most people do - get other opinions, all of which left me with more questions. Was the only solution prescribed medicine to be taken internally and applied externally – medicine which my research revealed had so many harsh side affects? I decided my life was out of control. I was in a state of emergency, feeling desperate to find answers, but where?

Corporate America was good to me; I had the finest of life and hospital insurance, new clothing and a car, the best of food and a great house along with this fabulous career. What I did have was zero education or training in the basic mechanics of my body. I'd always thought that if my body broke down, a doctor would fix me. Who in my world ever studied natural remedies? I had totally taken my body for granted as something that would never break down. Through the years I rarely got sick, and if I did, I generally worked despite feeling bad. Be strong! Sickness was a sign of weakness.

At age 37 my life would have been different if, when given the diagnosis, I had known then what I know now, namely how to treat my body with the same care, concern, training and respect that I dedicated to my job; how to develop innate wisdom along the way to notice the vital signs that my body was struggling or stressed, and if so, how to assist my body regain optimal health; how to understand the role stress, repressed emotions, trauma, accumulated anger, negative influences and self-talk play in lowering the immune system. Unfortunately I didn't have this information in my time of need in my first aid kit; if I had, I would have healed in 3 to 6 months rather than 7 years – a major part of my young life.

I made a decision that medication wasn't what I was lacking, and I decided to step up to the plate and get educated about my own body. Never again would I place myself in this helpless condition.

Over the next 6 years I ended up unable to work and unable to cover the boils on my bright red face with makeup. I became my own research specialist spending most days contacting and/or visiting medical doctors and holistic practitioners in hopes of getting answers. Here are some of the questions that I asked: How does anyone heal anything? If I scratch my arm and it heals, then why can't my face heal? If I have a healthy cell today and a diseased cell tomorrow – why can't the diseased cell reverse? If my face is approx. 5 % of my overall body and the rest of my skin looks fine – what is so different about my facial skin? I kept asking: "Have you seen anyone heal anything and if so, can I interview him?" Thinking the mechanics of the inherent healing process couldn't be that different for all people, I figured the body couldn't be as complicated as the experts working with clients every day led me to believe. Why was it such a secret?

In the meantime my money started running out and I willingly sold any and all the valuable possessions accumulated in my corporate career, to desperately bide my time in finding a cure.

By the 6th year I had progressively gotten worse. My strict diet, exercise program and self-nurturing to the best of my ability wasn't working. At age 42 my life looked as if it was over. My face was deformed, and I no longer could read or drive, as the disease had affected my eye sight.

I knew in my heart not to give up as I wouldn't know what I would have missed if I could heal. Determined, I moved forward. I felt fragile and scared and tried hard to portray to those around me that I was calloused enough and/or strong enough to endure Rosacea and the daily embarrassment of others seeing what I felt was an ugly face. There was no safe place for me to be myself since I was surrounded with people who either wanted to give me remedies or thought I had been in a fire and wanted all the details.

Finally, in the sixth year I met with an eastern medical doctor who specialized in understanding how our immune system heals and repairs. In one hour, he diagnosed me differently than all the others. His answers made sense and turned my life in a "right turn." He discovered I had an internal quiver which I experienced 24 hours a day. All my organs were out of harmony with each other from being traumatized from having this disease. In order to heal, he told me, I had to find peace within at whatever cost and allow my organs to go back to their natural rhythms. He also discovered in my medical history that I had taken 5 months of allergy shots. He told me he thought that the allergy shots had lowered my immune system; which then affected my entire body. It was right after the shots ended that I came down with Rosacea. He wasn't sure I would heal but that finding peace within would be a key factor.

At last I had found the solution to my health at the "cause level" and had been given hope in finding answers. No one in 6 years of interviewing others ever addressed the "whole person" approach which looks at both the emotional and physical components. Everyone up until then (including myself) looked at my face - "the effect."

I became aware of how emotionally traumatized I had become, starting with my first skin doctor. I innocently bought into the label of being "incurable" for lack of understanding, even though I fought accepting this label. Over the years, the label "incurable" had affected my overall health, my organs, muscles, skeletal body and my spirit. My internalized fear and worry had emotionally "choked down my life force" in a desperate attempt to shield myself from the emotional pain of having this disease.

I can only imagine looking back what my body felt like - a kitchen towel rolled lengthwise and then twisted tighter and tighter, so that there was very little oxygen flowing and extreme adrenal exhaustion. Scared stiff and traumatized from what I was experiencing, I shielded myself with many layers of armor. Like a robot I went through the motions of my daily life. I didn't cry the whole time I had Rosacea, but there was no joy and just a small flicker of hope to continue.

Healing cannot take place in a fearful, unhappy, stress-filled and tense body

After getting correct information from the eastern medical doctor and applying what I learned from him, I healed in one year without scars. The capillaries that had broken miraculously healed, and my eyesight returned.

I learn that in order for healing to take place the internalized trauma from years of having Rosacea had to slowly reverse itself. I had to go back to the natural state of my wonderful flexible body, allowing my life-force to regain harmony within and experience "peace within." Learning to relax, rest and find emotional support to heal took patience and ultimate self-nurturing to accomplish.

CHAPTER 4

The Remedy Lies Within

Taking my power back I move into being empowered and not helplessly fear filled.

From my living with Rosacea for 7 years, I know that trial and error doesn't work; it is all focused on getting better and then getting worse. This sets up a distrust of ever healing. I became disappointed with the imperfection and changes I was experiencing. I created an internal self-talk of fearing and hating my situation. Like a relationship that I no longer trusted and distanced myself from, my own body became my enemy and not my treasured best friend. This was caused by running aimlessly in fear rather than in faith.

I found, no one dare talk honestly about what it feels like to have a long term ailment or diagnoses. I had internalized anger, rage, fear and depression, roller coaster mood swings and endless self doubt that totally change the chemistry (like a poison) within my body. I could no longer "trust or love my body", having to daily lance boils and look in the mirror at my fire engine red face that felt on fire. I couldn't visualize what it was like to have a normal healthy facial skin. Added to this I had began to feel that somehow I was becoming damaged and un-repairable!

I eventually self-healed. I actually got to witness how my Rosacea and near blindness got reversed. Now years later, my quest has been to find out why the Rosacea got so extreme ...what was the emotional pain that showed up as an angry deformed bright red face and near blindness? The answers started being revealed when I was passionate and open to learn more from this frightening yet miraculous experience.

I began to question the sequence of events in order to find deeper answers. How had I, a corporate leader, when diagnosed with an incurable disease allowed it to traumatize me? The answer was that I had been totally unaware of how exhausted I was, and the diagnosis took me by surprise. I felt helpless with no tools to help myself and determined never to place myself in this situation again, and to learn everything I could about my body.

I started questioning my belief system. Had I decided it was okay to never find the time to nurture myself? Had my behavior over the years sub-consciously started convincing me I didn't measure up to those around me? Had my ugly face with Rosacea convinced me that my negative core belief was right, and thus pushed me over the edge?

I realized no matter how much I felt I had accomplished I couldn't really embrace my achievements. My life training taught me to be strong and not feel my emotions – not to cry. As a result, success did not have much feeling –no big deal! Now, I was questioning why, with all my talent, I had had such a hard time embracing my true worthiness? Perhaps I had a problem loving myself regardless of the accomplishments.

CHAPTER 5

Revealing the Hidden Hurts behind Rosacea

In order for me to be an effective and authentic emotional wellness coach and spiritual director, I feel I must lead from personal experience and example. I have been in my own recovery for years, healing my hidden hurts, losses and limited beliefs. This has made me more effective in helping others with these same issues and life experiences. I believe that when one of us heals, we can all heal.

I discovered a breakthrough in understanding why Rosacea and acne appear on the face. The face is what we show the world about how happy or unhappy we are inside. Why is this so significant? Nature doesn't lie! Although skin is the last place a health challenge will appear, it always comes from within, from our being out of harmony with nature. Perhaps it could be said that our hidden hurts have gotten under our skin. I was exhausted inside and worked over the top of it every day. What troubled me under my skin was the way I worked under high stress, determined not to feel my feelings at whatever the cost. Stifling my emotions left me very rigid in my daily routine - a perfectionist with no room for fun or error as I hid out in the corporate world with my work addiction. I hated my own self-destructive behavior but it was familiar and I felt like I couldn't stop as the next assignment demanded my time.

Quote from: Joy-Full Holistic Remedies, page 101
Chapter Title: Heal By Expressing and Connecting
"I don't believe there are enough pain killers, surgeries, drugs, addictions, or alcohol to squelch the various cries of emotional pain, negative body memories, and spiritual emptiness."

Let's go back to basics

First, I believe babies come into this world with an inherent purpose and passion, with a natural healing and repair process. I believe that we are brilliant and highly creative beyond measure when encouraged and loved in ways that enhance our very souls to grow... that having peace within and inner joy is very natural. Health and happiness are one and the same thing. We trust our bodies and minds to intuitively honor what we like and dislike.

As babies we could get angry, cry, wail and soon laugh ready to go play. We were born with a natural, inherent emotional release process. Our life training for some of us eventually teaches us to not feel, not to get angry or cry and take what was natural and shut it down – burying our feelings alive. When we take the natural and train it to be un-natural in the end it will prove to be very hurtful and harmful.

I believe the fulfilled, nurtured, totally loved and respected child rises to a healthy adulthood. A healthy child innately will want to and enjoy creating and will get bored when he is not. The areas that are incomplete or that have been taken away will leave the child with secret wounds, and brokenness will surface to be healed when the student is ready.

CHAPTER 6

Re-wind - How It All Started

In order to teach you what I've learned, I will reveal the rest of the inner work I've personally done since I wrote my Joy-Full Holistic Remedies book. I hope my example can help you find your own answers.

In my innocence as a child I took on some very hurtful false core beliefs. They became so familiar that over the years they were like a silent subconscious message; silent in that I wasn't consciously aware of how false and destructive they really were. It took a major health challenge and years of recovery work to help me gently surface these false beliefs about myself in God's timing.

False Core Beliefs create very unhealthy patterns of behavior that continue to repeat themselves in our current reality. Until we stop and look deeper at our own behavior, we'll always think the situation is about "the other person." It is in some spiritual, higher way because this person that we are blaming really is a gift that helps us crash and hit bottom one more time, hard enough that we will start to look within ourselves for answers. Hopefully we are hurting badly enough to be willing to do whatever it takes to heal – willing to heal our false core beliefs about ourselves and be set free of this vicious, very hurtful, very distrustful circle that for most of us started in childhood or as teenagers.

Here is a list of my false core beliefs in hope that you will discover at a deeper level your own.

I was the first born and showed up as a girl. I was told I was a disappointment to my father because boys could carry on his last name, along with eventually being in business with him.

Between age 3 and 6, I lost 3 siblings leaving me to grow up isolated and alone out in the country with my parents. None of us knew how to grieve. Silence became deadly, and work became the solution to not dealing with emotional pain. (Watch how I took this message of "work - don't feel" into my adulthood)

I was sexually abused at an early age and at age 14, date raped. I took on a belief of being ashamed of who I was as a child, young teenager and human being. I buried my feelings, voice and spirit alive, hiding my secret hurts.

By age 14 my false core beliefs was; I am not important, second best, women were to be 'used,' and there was not enough <u>fill in the blanks</u> to include me. This list eventually came up over and over again in my life in hiding out in relationships, jobs unhappy, lack of utilizing my creative talents, under earning and financial insecurity, too scared to change because feeling less-than was familiar.

Many years later my Rosacea face - as a bright red stop sign, called me out of hiding and revealed my face, body, mind and spirit to the world. Reclaiming that beautiful talented little girl inside and her true worth!

My voice teacher was my cheerleader who had me singing solos in the choir and kept praising me for the extraordinary voice I was developing at age 15. After one year of private lessons, this wonderful man died in a car accident. (I took on a belief that life was unfair and gave up, with no desire to ever sing again.) What I did with this new loss was shut down. I ended up not singing until 20 years later, when in a praise and worship church I questioned why I couldn't sing. I had been too busy working to notice this wonderful part of

my life was missing. Healing hidden hurts and waking up –
re-claiming the precious, playful, talented child inside of me
- has been my journey of transformation into a person I
dearly have grown to love and admire. (I now play guitar,
write music and sing.)

At age 16 I worked two jobs – some nights until midnight -
and went to high school. I was praised for working and I
totally neglected having any play time or fun. (Again I was
driven to not feel and felt I had some worth by my work
performance and making money. Work was my drug of
choice for staying numb. I was not aware that I was taking
on a work addiction that was as destructive as an addiction
to drugs or alcohol.)

At age 16 I discovered I could race my father's car with other
young people at extremely fast speeds and on dangerous
country roads. One night I raced with the wrong car. It was a
policeman and we were going close to 90 miles an hour.
Fortunately I only got a ticket. After that I slowed down.
(Racing cars was one way I could express my deep anger and
emotions by burning up the road)

I married 3 men who were emotionally unavailable, exactly
like my father. Two were extreme work alcoholics and

wanted a pretty lady by their sides and sex when the occasion called for it. The other one was a preacher who was a dry drunk and sex addict who treated me at home – outside the church - as though I didn't have a brain, reinforcing my brokenness. After divorces I've learned a great deal about healthy relationships and have gone to great lengths to study and heal in this area, of which I'm very proud.

Quote from: Joy-Full Holistic Remedies, Page 48

Marriage

"To be with someone who is willing to feel safe talking about secret thoughts and feelings gives the listener permission to learn something valuable about themselves and open up, accelerating the bonding and personal growth. Facts and feelings aren't twisted and held back as in surface conversation. The first step is to choose someone whom we consider our closest and dearest "friend," building a relationship of integrity, honesty, trust, and closeness, continually creating fun times together. Without this we live as strangers.... I wondered for years how marriages that look so materially sound could feel so empty."

We bury our false core beliefs about ourselves
in hopes no one will ever find out.
Not noticing they are running our lives!

Without healing our false core beliefs we carry them sub-consciously with us increasing the divorce rates and struggle through relationships, careers, health issues running aimlessly on empty. We learn to have self-talk about ourselves that we would be embarrassed to share with others – core beliefs that came directly from those tender years of growing up.

For the rest of my life, as a result of these subconscious false core beliefs, I experienced both failures and successes in life as proof that I wasn't good enough. I couldn't work enough or have enough success to ever fill my inner void. Yet, for years I felt an emotional void – that I was missing something. I find it hard to describe – like walking with a cloud in front of me blocking / shielding me from "feeling." I could intellectualize my success but I couldn't experience the feelings of success in the moment. I did anything and everything to work harder and become more successful, driven day and night. I didn't know I was doing all I could to avoid, hide or never feel my false core belief. Having Rosacea magnified my belief in not being okay. Rosacea helped me heal many areas of my life, including my work addiction, adrenal exhaustion, emptiness, sense of unworthiness, my love for self and God.

For most of my life I never showed anger, but looking back I'm sure the unfairness of some of the things that happened to me would make anyone naturally enraged. I think my being addicted to work was fueled and driven from my internalized anger and rage - which I did not feel, but even not feeling was a feeling. My rage got expressed physically in the red rawness of my Rosacea and near blindness, my years of internalized silent rage at what felt like the unfairness of life finally found a way to heal.

Notice that anything that is unlike our natural perfect selves – like stuffed emotions and hidden hurts – will eventually surface for healing in some shape or form. It will get pushed out of the body as part of our own transformation. I now see this transformation from beginning to end as all good, and move out of judgment or asking all the questions about "why this happened to me?" All my experiences have built my character and the gifts I'm able to share with others are all the areas I've experienced, learned and healed from. This is a vast resource of wisdom that I couldn't have learned in a university.

I carried hidden hurts and body memories from my past without being aware of them. Is it possible health challenges are our way of bringing these core issues to the surface for healing and clearing the way for our spiritual path along with freedom from the past? I believe this is the case. Like the transformation of the cocoon and the butterfly, in the cocoon state it is what it is, and healing takes whatever it takes, as long as it takes, in God's timing not mine.

Now, let me help you find your own answers!

CHAPTER 7

Health Evaluation – For Rosacea and Acne Going Beyond the Face

Finding answers, if you have Rosacea or Acne I want you to see that perhaps your own body has been much like that kitchen towel I explained earlier – rolled lengthwise and twisted from daily fear and anxiety. The stress hasn't developed over night but accumulated without your being aware. Keep this in mind as a key factor in your own healing. You have been *scared stiff* as the saying goes but have numbed your feelings in order to function in everyday life. This type of accumulated stress gets the body out of harmony and causes many random symptoms that can be healed once our body is encouraged to relax and do whatever it takes to bring the body back to a peaceful, restful condition. May I add, easier said than done!

I discovered after working with hundreds of Rosacea/acne clients definite indicators that others overlook because their search is isolated to the face. I have a saying, "The body is not complicated and the answers can be found by bringing the body back into natural harmony."

In my personal experience, **I don't believe you can heal Rosacea and acne without addressing these other or internal symptoms.**

Let's begin

Holistic Natural Remedies look at the emotional, physical and spiritual components of the "whole person" to solve any health challenge. Example: our skin is our largest organ and the last place to exhibit symptoms of health challenges; facial issues are affected by greater internal issues. While our expressions show our current emotions, our very skin shows how happy or unhappy we feel inside.

If you have been diagnosed with Rosacea and or acne, your health issue is a gift in disguise, redirecting your life. How would it feel to be educated about your own natural healing process so that you trusted your body and could solve almost anything when body changes occurred? Rosacea and acne generally appear on the face. Like a red stop sign, it urges us to stop, look at our whole selves, and re-evaluate life. By insisting on having nurturing, loving boundaries around ourselves, we will learn to live healthier and happier, in joy-full creative passion!

When we accumulate stress, fear, trauma and unhappiness, the human body will get random symptoms. These symptoms are our natural healing and repair process trying to get our attention, wanting to self-correct back to our inherent wellness or natural harmony. Too often, when this cry for help is ignored or misunderstood, the body is neglected and in some cases abused. The body continues to break down as long as its natural harmony is unbalanced. This feeling of disharmony becomes familiar to us, and we allow our health issues to multiply.

When we shift our focus from the face, there are the obvious indicators of internal disharmony that can be healed. Our skin simply reflects what is going on inside the body and mind. There are many areas in one's life to evaluate. I have based this health evaluation on the emotional and physical areas, which is usually where I start my search for answers.

Next I would like you to take the following health evaluation and, in order to heal, learn for yourself the importance of living in harmony within your mind and body. This will be an eye opener for many of you as you take your focus off your face and take an honest look at how to solve your own health challenge.

Consider any medications you use. Have you researched their side effects? Are you experiencing any of them? Educate yourself on what you are doing internally and externally to yourself. Take special caution.

<u>**Health Evaluation – For Rosacea and Acne**</u>: Take an honest look at yourself and answer the following questions. Your score is the number of times you answered "yes."

Emotional:

- Are you embarrassed about your looks, and do you tend to isolate?
- Do you have roller coaster mood swings along with depression?
- Have you been told that your condition is incurable? Have you agreed?
- Do you feel emotionally and spiritually empty?
- Are you sick and tired of being sick and tired?
- Do you distrust your body to heal?
- Do you feel anger, rage, or are you anxious about your health condition?
- Have you had losses you have not been able to grieve and heal? This can be people or pets, jobs, treasured items or abilities.

- Is your self-talk mostly that of fear and worry?
- Do you have high stress, chaos and turmoil externally and internally in your life?
- Do you act strong and pretend to be happy?

Physical:

- Do you find yourself exhausted often?
- Do you have hair loss?
- Do you have a short or long term internalized quiver?
- Does your skin appear to be getting more sensitive or thinner?
- Do you experience headaches often?
- Do you have TMJ jaw problems?
- Are your lips starting to turn white or lose their color?
- Do you grind your teeth?
- Do your feet hurt?
- Do you often find your stomach tense – tied in a knot?
- Do you experience nose bleeds?
- Do you have a history of constipation?
- Do you have indigestion?

Score Yourself

How many times did you answer "yes"?

1 to 5   Mild emotional/physical stress. Start taking positive steps to make changes.

6 to 10   Accumulated stress has started producing random symptoms. Make a commitment to change your results over the next 6 to 8 months.

11 to 24 Take emergency measures; evaluate what it will take to nurture yourself to the point of relaxing and finding peace within —whatever the cost.

Now that you know how stressed you are, what do you do? Each of these questions addresses an indicator that your body and mind are out of harmony, that your immune system and nervous system have mild to extreme stress. Once you are aware of these random symptoms, you can start healing them one by one. Interestingly, once you start relaxing and moving out of fear, many of these indicators will domino toward healing, correcting themselves.

If you feel overwhelmed with the results of your score and intuitively feel you are ready for additional help, I am available to teach you how to understand and correct your own personal indicators or symptoms.

Understanding the Evaluation

The most common reaction to acne, Rosacea, or any skin problem is fear. We are constantly reminded that our problem could get worse, and even when it does clear up, we may be labeled "in remission" and we brace ourselves from the thought of it coming back. Some days we want to run away from our reflection; counting boils and pimples becomes crippling.

This type of internalized emotional stress accumulates over time, with the pressure on our physical body ranging from mild to extreme. We tend to act brave and numb ourselves to our fear—so much so that we forget it's there at all. We become rigid in our skeletal body, and our blood pressure may go up. Concentration becomes difficult and breathing becomes shallow. Oxygen deprivation eventually – ever so slowly-- starts choking our life force. It happens to the best of us.

Since our body is approximately 70% water and another key factor is oxygen, every system is dependent on them. Once the body starts being deprived, our emotional stress can no longer be held internally, so it breaks out in depression, roller coaster mood swings, anger, and (of course) pimples. Our skin begins to reflect what is happening within us and we become embarrassed and isolate ourselves. We return to counting pimples in the mirror, fearing that our skin condition will become worse, and we spiral lower.

What happens to the skeletal body once we get scared stiff and try to walk through life normally while inside we are tense? We eventually apply enough inward tension on our body to cause hair loss, grinding of teeth, jaw problems, nose bleeds, constipation and indigestion. Extreme fear and stress causes our organs to get out of harmony with each other and causes an internal quiver. When we apply enough fear, anger and stress on ourselves it is not uncommon to complain about our feet hurting. Why? Stress affects our entire body. Our nerves, like hairs spanning across our bodies, start at the nape of our necks and carry energy through every organ in the body, ultimately ending in our feet. We have 7400 nerve endings in each foot, and all the excess stress flows to the end of the line.

When our focus has been on the face, we have missed a greater opportunity to look within for finding the real answer. Do a reality check right now. We know that if you scratch your arm and it heals, then your own inherent natural healing and repair process knows how to heal your acne and Rosacea. You can learn to trust your own ability to heal and move out of doubt. At first it may not be easy but as you learn to trust yourself over time, you will experience calm and stillness within.

Being aware of our behavior, we can start to help ourselves. Move out of fear. Start to enjoy your life and relax by nurturing and loving yourself. Affirm that your face is healing, and deliberately breathe deeper throughout the day. Exercise in moderation. Remind yourself often to relax and get quiet inside.

Since I have walked the path of having acne and Rosacea, I know I felt very alone during those 7 years. Let me teach you the basic mechanics of how your body does natural healing and repair, how to stay emotionally and spiritually healthy, and how to find and start living your creative passion. Be joy-filled and stop running on empty.

Begin healing now; try some of these suggestions:

Read my self-help book *Joy-Full Holistic Remedies, How to experience your natural ability to heal* and get my educational *CDs on various subjects - for steps to heal yourself*. See my web site: RosaceaHealedEmotionally.com and Joy-full.com

Find peace within at whatever price it takes to get it.

Eliminate those people and situations that don't warm your heart.

Stop researching the web sites that fill you with fear about your condition.

Do more of what you enjoy – read the chapter, "Measure Your Joy" in Joy-Full Holistic Remedies.

Stop labeling yourself with any health condition.

Stop all body hatred!

Make taking care of yourself your top priority – nurture your body through massage, yoga, and nature walks. Nurture your spirit through meditation and prayer. Nurture your mind through art, hobbies, and self-acceptance.

Maintain a good diet and exercise program, but know that neither will be enjoyed or of benefit if you are not emotionally happy within yourself.

The human body by divine design has water flowing much like a river throughout our body. We have been taught in our life training to go up stream – running on empty and forcing ourselves against the natural current. Unhappiness and emptiness lead to poor health. The truth is we are brilliant and wonderfully made and have a natural healing and repair system in place that works for us every day.

How does one begin to turn back to living in natural harmony within? First we become willing to learn a whole new way of living, trusting our bodies and intuition. Enhancing our lives by exploring wellness and natural remedies can be fun, educational, and very rewarding.

Take this opportunity to turn your life around. Heal, become empowered; stop living frightened and become enlightened. Eliminate trial and error and speed up your recovery with my system. My love of healing and helping others becomes obvious once you start working with me. I am available to teach you as your own emotional wellness coach and spiritual director. I will gently hold you accountable for moving forward. The time and money you spend will return to you over a life time in wellness.

Take your total focus off the things you fear and move into more praise and gratitude.

80% of your health issues stem from being unhappy within yourself. Start loving your body including your toes and fingers … Life would be different without them… Self love and appreciation are great healers.

Believe always that you can heal!

CHAPTER 8

Healing Core Beliefs

Ask yourself – what core beliefs do you believe about yourself? About your natural ability to heal? If you have been labeled with an incurable illness – what belief do you have about it?

Start writing your core beliefs about yourself and situation down on paper so you can start getting honest with yourself in making changes. Until you uncover any false core beliefs you might have, you'll continue the same pattern of experiences in your life.

In my book Joy-Full Holistic Remedies I have a whole chapter on how to write your history, I highly suggest you take time to reveal your own false beliefs and get them healed.

False core beliefs are sub-conscious negative beliefs that continually try to convince you you'll never heal, life is hard etc. This could be a major cause of your current behavior and lack of fulfillment. Here is a list of common false core beliefs:

Unlovable
Undesirable
Not worth loving
Not okay
You will never amount to anything
Irresponsible
Not pretty/or not good looking
Ugly
Just like my parents
Not good enough
Insignificant
Incurable
Unimportant
Underachiever
Something is wrong with me
Don't have what it takes to .....(heal)
Inferior
Flawed/broken
And the list goes on

How do we create true core beliefs about one self? Imagine a little orphan girl or boy who has been told these false core beliefs until he or she sub-consciously has believed them. We now adopt that little orphan girl or boy. If we continued to tell the child false core beliefs we would eventually break the child's spirit causing health, social issues and eventually addictions. Of course this wouldn't be helpful, would it? In order to heal false core beliefs we have to stop creating them and turn to affirming the child's goodness, enhancing the child's life with love and support. Making a positive U-turn and giving the child delighted attention where he starts feeling and experiencing its own worth. Notice I wrote *experiencing*, until we experience love and worthiness, we will never start to believe it. Now is the time to nurture our own self with the same respect as we gave the orphan child. We too have been neglected by ourselves and others, and it is past time to heal our false core beliefs and false self-images.

After you have evaluated your false core beliefs and decided to make a commitment to yourself to change – how do you start? Through self-nurturing and self acceptance; decide what brings your heart joy, fulfillment and respect. You might decide to start exercising and get your energy moving. Do new things and move out of being in ruts, bored and doing the mundane. Journaling helps get your thoughts on paper rather than staying in your head and getting re-played over and over. Getting your thoughts on paper gives you a fresh start at living more in the moment. Expand your talents by taking up new hobbies or classes that are creative. Many suggestions are found later on in this book.

If you have Rosacea /acne or other health challenges you can now stop fearing them. Take your focus off fear and into finding natural solutions within your body. Learn how your emotions and your physical body work in harmony with each other in a beautiful language. Try to speak and feel your very own truth. In the meantime you want to learn how you have been trained in your innocence to deny and trick yourself into not feeling. Once you have learned in slow motion how to "experience" a healthier way, you will not have to be tricked any longer.

CHAPTER 9

Rage Can Trick You

I'm going to insert here my insights on anger and rage. In our society it is not okay to show anger or rage. This has been instilled in most of us for most of our lives. Eventually, when either shows up, our minds are instantly trained not to allow either to be expressed. Our minds will divert us instantly by giving us pain or discomfort in our bodies. Our complete attention is directed to the pain, and the anger and rage get buried one more time. This has been a proven fact not only in my life but in my studies. We will go to any length to solve our physical health challenge, yet in the end nutritional supplements, medications and surgery still leave one most of the time with the same pain or discomfort. Anger and rage have not been addressed or admitted. They have been ignored, buried alive and are still screaming with pain, discomfort and many times depression. Tension from internalized anger and rage is often stored in the solar plexus area of the body. Unresolved tension affects all organs in that part of the body, particularly the colon.

Accumulated anger will turn to rage. I believe learning how to feel all of our natural feelings including these will set us free from many of our physical health challenges. The simplest thing when you first feel pain is to explore whether something has upset you. Are you feeling angry? Stop long enough to get in touch with what you are emotionally feeling and find ways to express these feelings rather than snuff them out. This gets exciting because it will keep you healthier and far happier. In the moment just admitting "I'm feeling angry or sad," or when someone says something hurtful saying, "I find that really hurtful" is often enough honesty to avoid the pain. I have a saying that we either work on our stuff (emotions, getting them expressed) or they will work on us physically.

Quote from: Joy-Full Holistic Remedies, page 76
Colon Care
"The whole body can be affected by the condition of the colon. The colon, or large intestine, is an elimination system that also serves to hydrate the body. When it malfunctions, you are sometimes unaware of the cause and experience unexplained aches, pains, allergies, sinus

problems, bad breath, indigestion, weight gain, bloating, constipation, cancer, etc." (Also includes skin issues)

"Tension from emotional events is often stored in the solar plexus area of the body, through which the transverse colon passes. Unresolved tension affects all organs in that part of the body, particularly the colon. As the colon muscle tightens, constipation results. Proper colon care not only helps to bring the body back into balance, but can also release stored emotions." (Plus improve and heal your skin.)

CHAPTER 10

Stuffed Emotions Will Reappear

The body never lies. If we are slighted, insulted, discouraged or not being true to our own selves or words, we may not acknowledge the physical random symptoms that follow, but the body will keep score. Stuffed emotions will accumulate and as our honest friend, in order to get our attention, will reappear in physical health challenges, or mild to extreme pain like a sore throat or headache. Notice this is different than the physical pain from just having a car accident.

Emotions are a language that once understood will help you see your daily life more connected to what is happening within your body and allowing your emotions to be delightfully expressed in appropriate free-flowing ways.

Here is an example of a few areas of the body where the emotions can manifest in physical health challenges - **which you can learn to release, reverse and heal.**

Rosacea, Acne and Facial Issues:
What I'm not willing to face. What I show the world about how confident, happy or un-happy I am within, physically and emotionally.

Lungs:
Not being able to grieve or cry, stifled, can't breathe fully, loss of joy, scared and suffer in silence.

Breast:
Serving others at one's own expense, emotionally and spiritually sucked dry, competition around breast size.

Heart:
Squeezing the joy out of the heart in favor of money, position or serving others or for another. Lack of self-love, joy and nurturing, making others more important, feeling broken hearted, stifled and bored.

Colon:
Tension, anxiety, sadness, anger, stress, rage. Holding in our own emotions and opinions for fear of displeasing others. Wanting to be in control. Staying in toxic relationships. Not wanting to help our own elimination. The colon holds our past memories, abuses and traumas.

Back:
Anger, financial issues, rage, disappointments and feeling burdened.

Prostate:
Pressure to continually perform to create money and success, until the tension in the body stops the natural fluid flow. Fear of aging and impotency.

Ankles, Knees and Hips:
Inflexibility, inability to bend or move forward in life.

Remedy: The next time you experience body pain, stop and place your hands on the area and direct love to it – as you would a hurting child. Get quiet and ask your body what it needs in order to feel better. Trust what you hear. Give this area delighted attention. It might tell you "You are sitting wrong in your chair and causing your shoulder to hurt" or "You are exhausted and need to rest." You will be amazed at how effective this is compared to our old way of ignoring it or medicating it in hopes the pain will go away.

Additionally: once you learn and experience how to stay healthy emotionally and physically, achieving optimum wellness – healthy and happy - something wonderful happens. Your body by divine design will abort or push out any of your emotionally accumulated negative memories (Notice they were never meant to be there in the first place), bringing you back to balance/center connected to your heart and feeling as if you just stepped into a healthy person's mind and body. This is not an unusual or rare experience. Nature by design is always calling us back to our true spiritual selves, our passion and what makes our heart sing.

Write your own prayer about your new belief. Here is an example:

Prayer: the Divine Intelligence within every cell and fiber of my body knows how to heal, repair and restore my body back to the perfection that has always been there. Even though I have _____ (list your emotional or health challenge here) _____, I deeply and completely love and accept myself. I move out of fear into faith, believing that "nothing is impossible with God." From this day forward I trust my body, mind and spirit to heal and live my passion with gratitude. I promise to get help, if that is what it takes to have support on my wellness journey.

CHAPTER 11

Clearing the Slate – Starting Over

I hope by now you are welcoming this new information and getting excited about all the wonderful possibilities you can "experience" for yourself.

Starting over, making up for loss years, here is my commitment and I invite you to make it yours.

- I can from this day forward totally love and accept myself.
- I will love my face and I'll do whatever it takes to be calm on the inside so my face can stay calm on the outside.
- I insist on being surrounded with people and situations that bring my heart joy.
- I will be with people and projects that enhance my life and not take away from it.

- My new core beliefs are I am worthy of the best, I was born worthy, I am enough, I was born enough and always will be.
- I am okay inside and outside.
- I love myself the way I am.
- I love and appreciate myself.
- What others think of me is none of my business – what I think of me is what counts!
- I am now free to live my creative passion!
- I realize I am brilliant beyond measure.
- I will seek ways to maximize my talents and spirituality.
- I am encouraging myself to be more creative and that means _____.
- I realize I've always done the best I've known how in any given moment.
- I will begin in baby steps to make positive changes so I don't get overwhelmed.
- I will learn and lead by example my new path of wellness.
- My false core beliefs are part of me. They will re-surface and I can compassionately see them for what they are ... false messengers.

I invite you to create a new path along with me

I love my new path which calls me to live what I believe and teach. The gifts of my spirit are to have peace within, harmony internally and externally, love for self and give others my overflow; to trust my intuition for yes and no answers; to create joy every day, moving away from what is boring and mundane. I now create art projects that warm my heart, not because I have to, but for the shear bliss of creating.

For me the gifts of my spirit are not suffering, fear, disease, illness, worry, lack, self-doubt and not okay-ness. Daily I take a closer notice of who or what is in my life and make changes where I feel necessary to get back on my joy-full track, staying away from chaos, which is very destructive when indulged in for very long.

CHAPTER 12

Finding Your True Self

Seek ye first the kingdom is about discovering a new way to appreciate and love our bodies and minds and all things will be added on to us. This is about feeling fulfilled, nurtured and empowered from within, giving others our overflow. It is about never again giving out of exhaustion and calling it love. Giving out of exhaustion will eventually lead to resentment.

Most of my life I was too busy to do art. My old way of thinking was, if it would never be a career then why explore it? One day at a silent retreat a very wise spiritual director told me the way to discover God was through art and invited me to go in the art room and spend the afternoon. Because of her years of helping others I respected her words enough to at least try. That afternoon I was shown how to move out of my busy mind and create, just for the sheer joy of doing it. At first I glanced at all the books available on making art, but I was wise enough to not seek more head knowledge. I picked up brushes and paints. I started out making a water color of how I was feeling in an art form. I remember I felt like a parachute that had collapsed and wondered what it would take to dialog with it, color it and get it to fly freely. It revealed to me I was needing more support. For me it was an amazing healing process. I still find it very revealing and inspirational.

From that afternoon, I pondered my dream as a teenager. I had wanted to be a fabric artist and design clothing. No one ever heard of being a fashion designer where I grew up. Soon after, I found a local class in Houston on how to paint on silk and since then I have had great fun creating some of my own clothing. I was invited to model my silk garments at a very large fashion show in Houston, Texas – it is never too late to have a happy childhood.

I tell my own breakthrough with creativity to encourage you to risk stepping out and playing more with art and hobbies. If you have had a long time desire to learn an instrument, water color, design clothing, sing, dance or design jewelry, now is the time to start taking action. Make it part of your therapy for self discovery and find your passion.

I love my spiritual life and the holistic approach to living. I have daily prayer time and try to stay in praise and gratitude. My home is surrounded with beauty and order. I live in silence a lot to get in touch with my intuition which I find is highly accurate when I move away from the distractions of the world around me. It's my non-compromising commitment to having peace within that allows me to be highly intuitive and effective when listening and helping others.

Nurturing myself is my top priority. There is so much to learn and create, more talent to uncover. It all begins when we are ready.

CHAPTER 13

Steps to Natural Healing

Number One

Stop. Imagine I'm with you and can take you by the hand, allowing you to feel how rare it is to learn from someone who not only healed from extreme adversities but also helped hundreds of others with various conditions just like you. Imagine me by your side to encourage you. Through my books and CDs you will have me with you 24 hours a day.

Number Two

Another option, if you prefer you can do personal consulting with me. Get a sense of how it feels to have your own mentor, spiritual director, guide and cheerleader, someone with whom you can share your inner most thoughts and feelings, someone with a listening ear and a heart filled with understanding giving you delighted attention. I have walked this path before you, so you can eliminate many of the mistakes I made along the way. Many choose one on one with me as a faster way to their own recovery.

Number Three

Breathe deeply with relief, knowing our very breath is a gift and there is no lack of oxygen in our world – or lack of answers to health challenges.

Number Four

Know that water and oxygen are vital to keep us alive – all flowing freely when not restricted. Explore the idea that once we fear the "label of the diagnoses," our minds ramble with fear and our body's life force gets choked down, trying hard to not feel our feelings. Soon we suffer from <u>oxygen deprivation</u>. It will happen to the best of us as we become fearful and scared. We must not sacrifice our own oxygen in fear. We must affirm "it is safe to breathe fully, and I'm being led to find natural healing answers."

Number Five

See any health challenges as our internal body language trying to get our attention and move us in a healthier, happier direction. See it as your friend not your enemy. Hidden hurts and emotional pain manifest in physical form and can be reversed, once heard and released. Emotions are not something to be "feared," not even when they have appeared in a physical form. Find local support groups, self-help books, CDs, DVDs and/or web sites that are positive and up lifting.

Number Six
Our negative self-talk has the ability to change the chemistry in our bodies in harmful ways because it is inherently unnatural to think this way and therefore your body will resist the unnatural. Fear, self-doubt, worry, rage, shame and distrust of one's self come from a "core belief" that something is wrong with you, all of which can be healed, and any type of body self hatred has to stop!

Number Seven
Our positive self-talk has the ability to transform and heal our lives. Since negative self-talk is more familiar, the good news is once we become aware of how by comparison they both "feel" inside our bodies, we can make healthier choices. This goes beyond positive affirmation. This is about healing our core beliefs about ourselves.

Number Eight
The question is sometimes asked – are we chosen to suffer or have we done something in our past to have caused our Rosacea or acne? We are chosen to find the 'gift' in all of this that we learn from going through this experience of how to nurture and appreciate ourselves in ways we would have never learned at a university or reading a book. Like the butterfly emerging from the cocoon, we, too, are in transformation and our old ways of thinking, of relationships

and careers we are being asked to let go of. What no longer serves us or lowers our energy must be honestly looked at and positive changes made. The gift we receive through our own healing experience teaches us a deep respect and love for ourselves that we will protect at all cost. It is called *having boundaries*.

Number Nine

Forgive yourself for thinking there was something wrong with you or somehow you are not okay. Look at your baby pictures and decide - from this day forward this baby deserves to be loved and cared for with the highest respect for self.

Number Ten

Grow spiritual roots. Find ways to get quiet within for 5 to 20 minutes or more preferably twice a day and have a daily ritual where you open to your higher self to God and remind yourself of things you are grateful for. Take time to appreciate yourself from head to toe and how wonderfully you are made. Love is still the greatest of all remedies. Adopt a way to walk through life calmly. Let your peace within radiate outward on your daily journey.

CHAPTER 14

Daily Priorities – Faithful to Self

- Take time to become peaceful within and do whatever it takes to include this in your life.
- Eliminate being around negative people, situations and media.
- Focus your attention on your own healing as if in an emergency. Neglect yourself no longer.
- Embrace your 'true self' and never give false core beliefs your precious energy.
- Stop serving others at your own expense.
- Find local or web site support that is positive and up lifting.
- Maximize your own talents, getting on with your life.
- Eliminate chaos and clutter. Create beauty and order to represent yourself well.
- Cultivate your playful side. Find careers and hobbies that bring you joy.
- Remind yourself that you might have been addicted to suffering because it was familiar. Decide to heal self-abusive behavior.

- Expect and require that situations and relationships be enjoyable.
- Listen to your intuitive inner voice regarding what is good for you, right for you, and then follow it.
- Diet and exercise are part of our recovery list. Neither will be enjoyed or of benefit if you are not emotionally happy within yourself.
- Find a way of making money that you enjoy, and your money and life will be a blessing.
- Find ways to save money for yourself and 'security fund' for your future dreams and/or emergencies
- Pray without ceasing. Stay in gratitude.

My Articles for You to Enjoy

Write Your Story and Heal

Take Care of Number 1

Heal Your Work Addiction!

Write Your Story and Heal

The monk, who looked like Santa Claus, offered to pray with me. Four days into a week-long silent retreat, I welcomed the opportunity to talk with someone. Never did I imagine the incredible physical, emotional and spiritual healing that would take place as a result of our conversation. In sharing my story, I invite you to claim this same healing for yourself.

As we talked, I told him how I had been healed from a disfiguring, deforming, "incurable" facial skin disease called Rosacea by using natural remedies. He acted as though he didn't hear me! Instead, we had a long conversation about monastery life, and then he went into a long spell of silence.

Just as I was beginning to wonder if "this is all there is," he opened his eyes. With a piercing stare and a deep, authentic tone of voice he said, "God has spoken to me – God has not healed you to keep it a secret. You must write a book and share your story."

Surprised, I told him I wasn't a writer, didn't have money to hire a writer and perhaps years from now I would get around to getting it done. He continued to repeat in his kind, godly voice: "God has spoken. You must write your story." I thanked him and immediately dismissed the idea.

Two months later, the unexplainable happened: the arches of both my feet fell. In pain, I told my clients I would be back in two weeks, but never returned. It became obvious that my friendly monk was correct, and beyond my excuses there was an urgency for me to write my story.

First, I wrote every memory I could recall, looking honestly at why I had served others at my own expense until my dear friend, my body, stopped my work addiction with a disease. I wrote day and night for seven months; never had I taken quality time to be with myself in this way.

Meanwhile, as I continued to write, the problem with my feet disappeared into the nothingness from which it came.

An incredible healing was taking place, and like pulling a thread on a tapestry, the more I wrote the more was revealed. Memories poured in, and life started making sense, especially when I started to see what I had been through and how I had healed despite the odds given me by more than 50 doctors.

The result of this writing was the self-help book I had looked for in my time of need but couldn't find: the details of how someone had healed. I remembered how desperate I had been to learn how natural healing takes place, how emotions manifest as physical ailments and how these can be reversed, and how to use my own discernment to direct my decisions. I had longed for a book I could pick up when depressed, fearful, or lonely to help me believe I could heal and find my purpose and joy.

Months later, readers of my book began sending me letters, telling me how the book was helping them. "I know if you could heal so can I," said Silvia from Venezuela. "Thank you for being brave enough to share your experience with all of us," said Judy from Japan.

I now encourage others to write their stories, mainly to help them heal their own lives. Many have miracle healing stories about what God has done in their lives and may have a burning desire to share those stories out of gratitude.

Writing your story will provide great insights about how you carry your past with you as you look at your beliefs, patterns, and joys. This is not about reliving the past; it is about creating a new life. I suggest writing in small increments, because for some of us our stories can feel overwhelming. Allow this to be a gentle learning experience.

As you write, take notice of any painful emotions that reveal themselves, because it is time to stop ignoring and denying them; instead, you can begin to heal and release them. Rewrite your memories over and over, if necessary, and discuss them with a safe friend. By acknowledging all of your story, you support your well-being mentally, emotionally, spiritually, and physically.

You may feel called, as I did, to share your story in book form. I named my book *Joy-Full Holistic Remedies*; this book, along with my healing, is a miracle.

Like the monk who encouraged me, I invite you to write your stories and heal.

Take Care of Number 1

Proud, to be physically healthy! Maybe one day, though, we notice we're feeling frazzled. Perhaps we're feeling heartburn, headaches, and stress, or have become physically ill. Suddenly we want to scream, pushing through our exhaustion as we pretend nothing's wrong.

Even when we're doing the work we love, we can experience burnout, and if we don't listen to the signals of our bodies, we can become physically ill. Even a case of the flu is a signal that our natural biological rhythms are no longer in harmony.

We persist at work that doesn't serve us; and stay in jobs, business situations or relationships when we know they are not enhancing our lives.

We hide in jobs and under earn not taking care of number 1.

If we're overworking ourselves, eventually exhaustion, anger, and resentment will set in. By taking good care of ourselves, we can stay healthy and retain our joy, fun, and excitement.

Following are some simple suggestions:

Ask yourself, does this job, relationship etc. serve me and/or enhance my life?

Commit to finding the joy and spiritual fulfillment gained from using your God-given talents and skills to better yourself and humanity.

Periodically ask yourself, "Am I breathing fully and deeply?" When we're in a hurry, our breath becomes shallow, causing knots in our stomach and starving our body of its basic need for oxygen.

Space appointments with you in mind. Include down time in your schedule, and keep that appointment as you would any other.

Avoid popping pills to sleep. Instead, spend time at the end of the workday in stillness and silence. Watching the news will not help you sleep restfully! Quiet time will help your body restore the natural rhythms disrupted by a busy day.

Walk, don't run with fists clenched and jaws strained. Move your body in a relaxed, fluid way.

If you think you need pain relievers, cigarettes, alcohol, caffeine, junk food, or sex, question your own behavior. If you have 'stuffed' hidden hurts and now have taken on addictions to numb your inner pain, you have piled one hurt on top of another hurt. Decide you deserve better and make the necessary changes. Reach for help if you need it.

When eating, pause to enjoy the experience. Choose fresh fruits and vegetables whenever possible, and chew your food thoroughly to release tension in your jaws, to encourage proper enzyme intake, and to prevent acid reflux. Remember to drink plenty of pure, filtered water.

Do nothing else while eating. Use this time to refresh and rejuvenate yourself.

Learn self-massage to treat discomfort or tension.

Schedule a massage, lounge in a jacuzzi, or stroll in nature.

Massage therapy or other forms of bodywork can take your body on a mini-vacation and improve productivity.

Sea salts and essential oils are great for the bath. They can be purchased at any health food store and provide relief for aches, pains, and stress.

Do you need to delegate more? Do you need to hire an additional employee or helper to be more effective in assigning tasks to others?

Positive self-talk and an attitude of gratitude are good for the soul.

Be non-judgmental, for you see others through your own eyes. Seek and see only good; it will reflect who you are.

Remember to schedule regular time for exercise, family, friends and hobbies.

Seek trusting yourself and life. Believe that only good is happening despite appearances. The greatest rainbows follow the worst storms.

Set personal goals for staying healthier and be proud of keeping your promise – to yourself!

Nurture yourself with great love and respect

Remember to say no! If someone tries to schedule you for engagements for the week you are on vacation or a retreat simply say you are already committed. Chances are they'll be impressed you are taking care of number 1.

When travelling out of town by yourself, bring pictures of family and friends to create a cozy, warm atmosphere in your hotel room. Consider packing a blanket and/or a small pillow.

Daily when away from home, pack healthful snacks, including some aromatic herbal teas, eat "real" food and remember to drink water.

Our bodies speak in a language of feelings and sensations separate from our thoughts. Headaches might be telling us to rest, drink water, or change something that is making us unhappy. Sinus problems may indicate we are stuffing our emotions. Weak eyesight may be a sign of unhappiness about what we see in our lifestyles, or perhaps we are spending too much time in front of the computer or television.

In our rush and stress, has self-worth or spirituality gotten lost in the shuffle? Take the time to find peace and harmony within yourself.

Disease occurs when we lose contact with the body's underlying intelligence responsible for maintenance, healing, and repair. Unfortunately, the body must, at times, get our attention through pain, illness, and disease. By breaking our agreement with the body, we become ill.

Keeping vitality, passion, and creativity alive can improve our health as well. Even the most rewarding work can feel dull if we don't nurture that spark within us. When faced with a decision, try using the "Measure Your Joy" scale. Look at your choices and rate your feelings about them from a scale of 1-10, with 1 being low energy, stress, resistance, and numbing, and 10 being complete happiness, health, and joy. This helps us connect with self-integrity and boundaries.

Healthy lifestyles are possible. They begin as we make the choice to nurture ourselves within so we don't compromise our health and happiness.

Heal Your Work Addiction!

Work at one's own expense is a sign of love, loyalty, obligation, co-dependency, service and financial security. For the overachiever, work addiction often goes unnoticed by top management or family members. A standard is set in which overachievement is expected and even encouraged by others such as employers, family members and even volunteer workers.

People take pride in their daily work and when the "rush for success, being needed or crises" is factored in, it becomes the ultimate test of an ability to produce results and to withstand extreme stress. The human body has a built in incredible fight or flight response. Much like buildings have fire alarms, both are intended for rare occasions. The workaholic continually "burns-out" this system with the thrill of being strong enough to endure handpicked for the next assignment or crises. Businesses praise and even lavishly compensated, the person's internal need to always be needed now pushes this addiction forward.

To overwork on whatever "it" is a temptation that cannot be rationalized against the importance of health or relationships with loved ones. Because most everyone has financial obligations that increase at the same pace as the rate of success, it's often not a choice.

Work addictive behavior is a false feeling of worthiness that often ends in empty devastation when the workaholic becomes unemployed or diagnosed with a disease. A person that has a compulsion to stay busy finds it almost impossible to relax or indulge in the luxury of having a quiet mind and body.

For a individual, family or corporation, the ultimate definition of "success" should be that we live in healthy, happy bodies. In the long run, it benefits everyone in terms of morale, reduction of sick leave and lower health insurance premiums. But this type of attitude must be embraced. Everyone can start teaching by example. If that is not possible, then individuals and companies can get involved in training seminars and education classes that teach how to live healthier more balanced lifestyles at home and in the office.

Solving health challenges brought about by stress is much like solving any business problem. First, identify the problem and people involved. If it happens to be a work addiction, admit the fact that it has gotten out of control. Ask and receive outside help if needed. Look at eliminating clutter and lessen the perfectionism standards, which go hand-in-hand with the numbing effect of the workaholic. Make a goal of having people experience peace within at whatever price it takes, which may mean reassigning and cross training employees, volunteers and/or family members. Attend meetings or invite in a combination of experts directed at understanding and healing addictive behaviors. Get personalized work done with an emotional wellness coach such as Georgie Holbrook. Start exercise programs. Start with making small changes over a period of time. If the program fails today - start over tomorrow.

The main cause behind burn-outs and break downs are pent-up emotions, un-happiness and stress that has manifested itself as physical symptoms. Our society tends to drug the symptoms, but if the cause had been recognized and released many times the physical problems will take care of themselves.

The cause and effect of burn-out and stress

We have at the cell level a biological system with rhythms for healing, repair and maintenance that consistently keep us healthy. Regular scheduled sleeping and eating patterns compliment this system. Headaches are generally caused from needing water, lack of deep breathing and not enough breaks. The cause can also be toxic smells, loud noise, lack of fresh air, vision strain or stressful situations.

Further suggestions:

Start teaching yourself to notice, by often scanning your body, to get a felt sense of any discomfort, pain or tension. If you find some tense spots, to make a choice to stop, take deliberate action to relax, breathing deeply and taking a break. It is amazing what a few minutes of self-care can do. Recognizing joy and health will increase success and profits with less effort and stress.

For a person who tends towards being a workaholic (one who has an inability to recognize or admit a destructive behavior) this type of situation can be like a smoldering brush fire. Denying stress and personal needs becomes a way of life, perpetuating a downward spiral. It is time to re-evaluate some of the cause and effects of burnout, stress, physical health challenges and un-happiness.

Heal your work addiction while you can
the life you save may be your own!

Find a way of making money that you enjoy,
and your money and life will be a blessing.

God has blessed us with each other.

Keep the Faith and Keep in Touch!

Blessings - from my heart to yours.

Love YOU!

Georgie

About the Author

Georgie Holbrook is an emotional wellness coach, spiritual director, and author. She has taught in universities, colleges, businesses, and churches. She teaches from her own experience and working with hundreds of others by phone around the world or in person. Her healing articles are published in numerous magazines.

Capturing worldwide attention, her books and CDs are easy-to-use guides to achieving physical, emotional and spiritual health. Georgie is receiving international acclaim for her self-healing discoveries.

Georgie examines the underlying needs of the human body differently than most, making the connection between our many physical health challenges and our habit of 'running on empty emotionally.' In addition to emotional and spiritual health she works with science/nutritional labs that have multi-patented, clinically proven products that optimally assist our own ability to heal.

Georgie teaches from experience. When she was diagnosed with acne that later became Rosacea, a disease an estimated 45 million suffer from, she was told by medical doctors and holistic health practitioners that it was incurable. In 6 years, her face was disfigured and she was near blind. Nonetheless, Georgie was determined that the natural healing process could not be that complicated and eventually found her own answers. With her newfound wisdom, she healed in one year without scars and her eye sight returned better than ever.

Author of: *Joy-Full Holistic Remedies, How to experience your natural ability to heal*

CD Titles: Each CD includes information on how to heal Rosacea & Acne along with other health challenges

- How Emotions can Heal Rosacea & Acne
- Guided Imagery, Dialog & Art for Healing Rosacea/Acne
- How Colon/Liver Health can Heal Rosacea & Acne
- Diet for Rosacea, Acne
- How Your Body at the Cell Level can Heal Your Face
- Healing Skin Disorders – A TV Interview

For additional information on her products and services visit Georgie's web sites:

RosaceaHealedEmotionally.com

Joy-Full.com

E-mail: Georgie@Joy-Full.com

CPSIA information can be obtained at www.ICGtesting.com
Printed in the USA
LVOW080541250412

279062LV00001B/9/P